The London Treasure Trail

This edition published in 2017.
ISBN 978-1-908921-07-9

First published 2012, reprinted 2015, 2017 by **Step Outside Guides.**

Printed and bound in Great Britain by Hertfordshire Display plc.

Acknowledgements

Our sincere thanks to the following people:

Derrick Hudson, the creator of Baby Tembo, for allowing us to use his little elephant.
Those who have trialled the trail for us:
The Froome, Hall and Palmer families and Phoebe Skinner.
Miranda and Duncan Brown, Joanne Ross and Teresa Solomon
for their encouragement and expertise.
Vicki Harris for editing our revised edition.

A special thank you to Sam for bringing Baby Tembo to life.

The London Treasure Trail

for Malcolm and Martyn

A Step Outside Guide

CONTENTS

Travel Tips

● Travelcards give unrestricted travel on buses, trains and the Underground any time after 9.30am on weekdays, and all day at weekends.

● If you are travelling from outside the Travelcard area, ask at your station for the best way of including central London buses in your ticket (it may be cheapest to buy a bus ticket separately when you get to London).

● Tube maps are available free at every Underground station.

● The Transport for London website is *www.tfl.gov.uk*

Introduction

Hello! My name is Baby Tembo, and I live here in London. I'm from Africa, as you can see by my magnificent ears, and my name is African, too – tembo is Swahili for elephant. Mr Derrick Hudson created me in 2006 and he has kindly allowed me to be your guide on our London Treasure Trail.

Today I want to take you to all sorts of lovely places, including the sparkliest street in London and a house with a whole world of treasure inside it. I'm going to show you where I live, and we're going to finish up at a garden in the sky!

We're not going to rush – it's much nicer and more interesting if we take our time. We're going on two bus rides, and for the second, longer ride I have made a special Bus Ride Guide to help you spot things as we go by.

Look at pages 6 and 7 to check you have everything ready, and then we're all set for a terrific day out together!

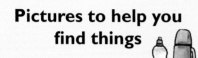

How to use your book

Pictures to help you find things

Good picnic spots

Accessibility information for buggies and wheelchairs

Free toilets

Top Treasure Alert!

You are about to see one of my special things or places!

Tick the jewel when you have seen it.

What to wear or bring with you

Comfortable shoes

Your picnic

Pencils and pens for *Rest-your-legs* pages

Your camera

Binoculars if you have some

Clothes and extras that suit the weather

IMPORTANT SAFETY INFORMATION

- Remember that London is very big and very busy; drivers can be fast and impatient.
- Only cross the road at traffic lights or pedestrian crossings.
- Make sure your group stays close together – no-one wants to get lost!

Roadworks

In a city there are often roadworks and building repairs going on. A building we've mentioned may be behind scaffolding, or a road closed. This is unpredictable, so it's best to just take it as part of London life, and enjoy any diversions. You may even discover something wonderful. Let us know at **www.stepoutsideguides.com**

Useful information and accessibility

Buses
All buses can accommodate wheelchairs, except the old Routemasters.

Kensington Roof Gardens
Entrance at 99 Derry Street
W8 5SA
Tel 020 7937 7994
www.roofgardens.virgin.com
Lift access.

Important:
• The Gardens may be closed for a private function; check by phoning up to one week ahead
• Photo ID is essential

Hatton Garden
Many shops are open at weekends, but may be closed on bank holidays.
Check on
www.hatton-garden.net

Sir John Soane's House
13 Lincoln's Inn Fields
WC2A 3BP
Tel 020 7405 2107
www.soane.org
Open Tuesday–Saturday
10.00am–5.00pm
Closed Sunday, Monday.

Ring ahead of your visit to enable staff to help you with access to the museum.

READY, STEADY, GO...

Starting Point:	Chancery Lane Station
	Central Line
Finishing Point:	Kensington High Street Station
	District and Circle Lines
Walking Distance:	About 5km
Time:	5 hours at a leisurely pace

To start our day, we're going to leave Chancery Lane Station by exit 2, 'to Holborn Circus'. Now set off along High Holborn past the HUGE red-brick Prudential Insurance building on our left.

Can you spot the elephant in the decorations? We can walk right into the splendid courtyard to have a look if you like.

High Holborn is a funny road – look down the middle of it. There are masses of bikes and motor-bikes parked there, with statues in amongst them, and some very grand toilets (which always seem to be closed – how silly!)

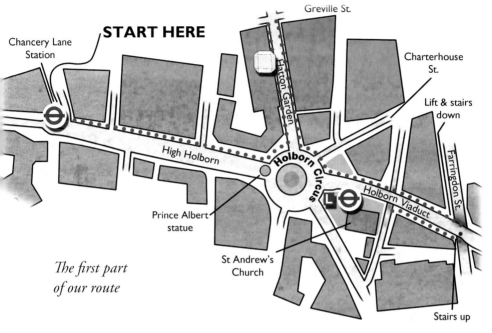

START HERE

Chancery Lane Station

Greville St.

Charterhouse St.

Lift & stairs down

High Holborn

Hatton Garden

Holborn Circus

Farringdon St.

Holborn Viaduct

Prince Albert statue

St Andrew's Church

The first part of our route

Stairs up

Prince Albert raising his hat

Holborn Circus

Very soon we arrive at Holborn Circus, which is just a road junction, and not a real circus – what a shame! There is a statue of Prince Albert (Queen Victoria's husband) at the edge of the junction, seated on a horse and raising his hat. If you've got a hat on, you can raise yours in return – but I'm afraid you can't do it with your trunk, like me.

HATTON GARDEN

Outside Holts, the shop at number 98, is a great big **geode**, or crystal cave. The purple crystals are amethyst, and this is how they naturally 'grow'.

The very first road to our left (at Holborn Circus) is Hatton Garden, and this is my first treasure – real treasure shops!

They aren't exactly hidden away, but although we are right in the middle of London, this is not a busy street. It doesn't look very spectacular, but just wait until you look in the windows.

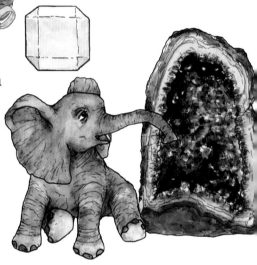

 We're going to walk up the left-hand side of Hatton Garden as far as the junction with Greville Street. We'll find my first **Top Treasure** on the way.

Aren't they beautiful! I think it is even prettier than the gemstones in the windows, though it can't be worn.

Many of these shops stay open at the weekend, but check *www.hatton-garden.net* on bank holidays as all the shops may be closed.

This road is named after Sir Christopher Hatton. Queen Elizabeth I gave him the land in 1576.

Who can spot the most expensive piece of jewellery? How much does it cost?

This area has been the centre of London's jewellery trade since medieval times.

There are zillions of pounds' worth of jewels in Hatton Garden. They must be VERY closely guarded. But there aren't lots of policemen or security people around. I wonder how they keep all this treasure safe. What do you think?

What colour gemstone do you like the best? My favourite is peridot.

Who has spotted the biggest jewel?

Peridot is a gentle green colour. It can be found all over the world.

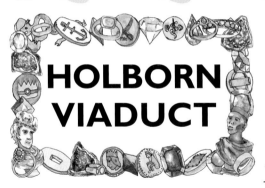

HOLBORN VIADUCT

See if you can find this dragon on the viaduct

When we get to the junction with Greville Street, it's time to cross the road and walk back to the Prince-Albert-and-his-hat statue, passing more treasure shops as we go.

Back at Holborn Circus, we need to cross Charterhouse Street, on the left, then walk a little way along Holborn Viaduct.

> ### Holborn Viaduct
> I love this bridge-road – or is it a road-bridge? It was built in the 1860s. The Victorians really knew how to build in style.
> The decorations are spectacular too: there are dragons, and helmets with wings – how odd!

Just before the second set of dark red railings, there is an elegant white building. We're going through its arch and down the stairs or lift to the street below.

St Andrew's Church in the 1860s

There is a huge and fabulous picture on the stairwell wall. Can you see what it's all about? It shows the viaduct being built. I bet there were a lot of 'horse jams' while that was happening!

On the left of the picture, look out for the square church tower. This is St Andrew's church at Holborn Circus. We are going to see the real one in a few minutes.

Before that, we can walk right under the viaduct. So, out on to Farringdon Street we go, and turn right. Look up at the struts supporting the viaduct.

The dragons and all the other decorations are beautiful. The outside looks magnificent, but the inside struts are jolly dirty.

It must have looked wonderful when the viaduct was clean and new. I think I'll give it a quick wash!

When we get to the other side of the viaduct, we will find another set of steps which take us back to the top. Look out for four red dragons, and lots of faces watching us. How many can you see?

St Andrew's Church now

If stairs are difficult, you can go back to the lift by the big wall picture, and then cross the road at the top.

At the top of the stairs, turn right and have a look at the top of the viaduct as the busy Farringdon Road traffic roars below. Then we turn around and walk to the bus stop labelled 'L'. It's right by St Andrew's Church, which we saw in the big wall picture.

It's time for our first bus ride! We can jump on any of the buses that come along.

We can take a break in St Andrew's Churchyard.

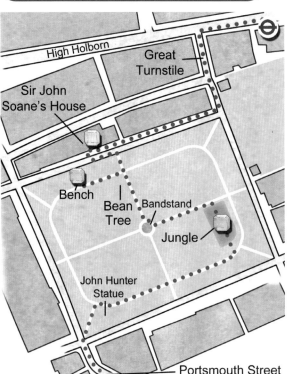

The third stop, **Brownlow Street**, is ours. Listen out for the announcement. It's right outside a cake shop, called 'Paul'. Hmmmm… if only baby elephants ate cakes!

Once we're off the bus we walk on, past the pub called 'Penderel's Oak', and immediately turn left into **Great Turnstile**. At the end of this little street we find ourselves in **Lincoln's Inn Fields**, and near our next treasure.

We need to turn right and walk about halfway along, to Sir John Soane's House at number 13.

We may have to queue for a little while to get in, but it is worth the wait to see this **cornucopia** of treasures.

GT TURNSTILE
Leading to
LINCOLN'S INN FIELDS

Great Turnstile. What a brilliant name for a street! Hundreds of years ago, when cattle grazed in Lincoln's Inn Fields, there was a turnstile here to stop them wandering out into busy High Holborn.

The Great Turnstile probably looked rather like this

Sir John Soane lived from 1753 to 1837, and he was an important architect. He designed the Bank of England, and there aren't many buildings more important than that! All his life he collected fragments of ancient buildings, paintings, sculptures, drawings and lots of other stuff besides – as you will see.

Sir John Soane's House is open from Tuesday to Saturday, and from 10.00am to 5.00pm.
It is closed on Sundays and Mondays.
www.johnsoane.org

SIR JOHN SOANE'S HOUSE

I am really excited about showing you inside here! We have to be VERY careful in the house because there are lots of wonderful but fragile things. I have to remember not to swing my trunk.

Although it is called a museum, the house is almost exactly as it was when Sir John lived in it about 200 years ago.

First we walk through the elegant dining room and library.

There is an astronomical clock near the window. Can you see the model of the planets moving around the sun at the top of the clock? How wonderful!

Teasel heads on the chairs remind us not to sit on this old and fragile furniture. It's definitely not made for elephants – even baby ones.

As we walk into the next room, the house becomes magical. Sir John's house is crammed with wonderful things – statues and carvings, models and paintings, urns, fragments of ancient buildings, stained-glass windows and even an Egyptian sarcophogus (coffin), covered in hieroglyphs. It all looks rather like a film set! What kind of film do you think might be made here? You can write a title in the space below.

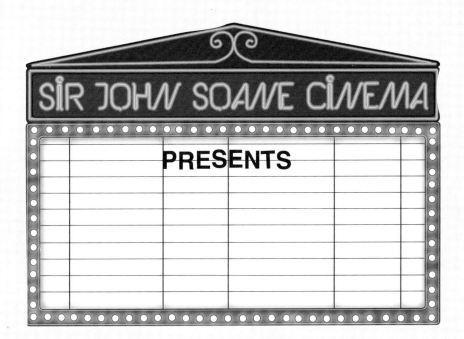

The **Picture Room** is my next **Top Treasure.** Although it is small, it contains more than 100 large pictures. How can this be? If we are lucky, there will be someone from the museum here to show us how all the walls swing out to reveal other pictures hidden behind. And these aren't just any pictures – some of them are very famous and important. One wall has three layers of pictures hidden away! So this is my hidden treasure, hidden in a hidden treasure.

Look up!
Don't forget to look up – some of the ceilings are richly decorated, while others are made of coloured glass, which casts a gentle light on all the treasures inside.

Top Treasure!
What is your Sir John Soane Top Treasure? Write it here:

Name

Baby Tembo

Your **Top Treasure**

The Picture Room

Phew! That was fantastic, but now, it's definitely time for a break, and maybe a picnic too. My lunch is a big bunch of bananas!

Let's leave Sir John's house, cross the road and go into the square opposite by the nearest gate.

LINCOLN'S INN FIELDS

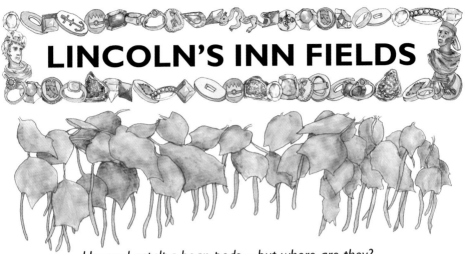

Unusual catalpa bean pods – but where are they?

Turn right, and we'll see a seat with a bronze sculpture of a lady and children along the top.

This is dedicated to Margaret Macdonald 'who spent her life in helping others'.
What a lovely way to be remembered!

Even now, after her death, she is helping people to rest. This is a nice spot for lunch, but if it's full there are plenty of other places we can sit. Turn over for our rest-your-legs page.

Rest-your-legs page

How many of these words can you find in my jewel word search?

AMETHYST, DIAMOND, EMERALD, GARNET, GOLD,
NECKLACE, PERIDOT, PLATINUM, RING, RUBY,
SAPPHIRE, SILVER, TEMBO, TOPAZ

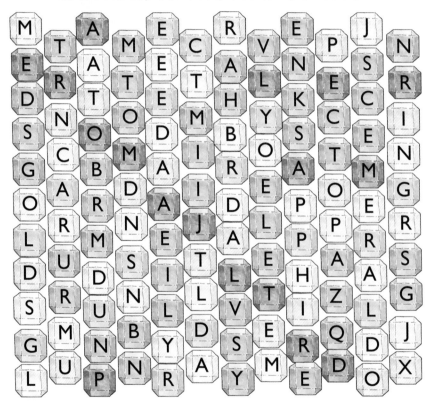

solution to puzzle p.32

What would you like to give me
for lunch? Draw it in my trunk!

Are you rested and revived? It's time for us to get up and on to find some more treasure, right here in the square.

A plane tree trunk – it looks like an elephant's trunk!

Where we came into the square is a catalpa tree. It has hundreds of HUGE bean pods hanging down. Can you see them?

It's a **jungle**! Home at last. It is not very big, but I love it here; it is so lush and overgrown, it feels as though there should be wild animals here too.

Catalpa tree with bean pods

From the tree, we're going to walk to the centre of the square, where there is a bandstand. Shall we pretend to be a band? I could play the trumpet! Turn left, and we'll pass under a gigantic old London plane tree. Can you see just how far the branches stretch out? Near the end of the path is a little turning to the right, and here is my next **Top Treasure.**

Which animal would you like to meet?

....

Which animal would you NOT like to meet?

....

FINDING TEMBO

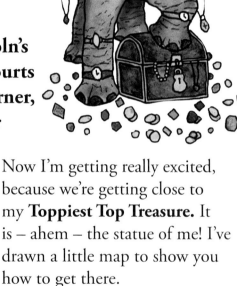

When we have safely trekked through the jungle, we are going to walk right across the side of Lincoln's Inn Fields, past the tennis courts and out of the gate in the corner, by the statue of John Hunter (see the map on page 14).

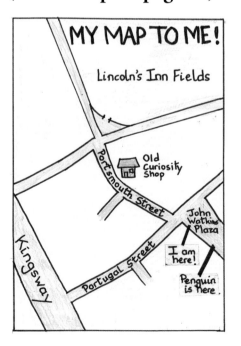

Now I'm getting really excited, because we're getting close to my **Toppiest Top Treasure.** It is – ahem – the statue of me! I've drawn a little map to show you how to get there.

When we leave Lincoln's Inn Fields, go down Portsmouth Street, which is almost straight ahead. Just where Portsmouth Street bends, we pass The Old Curiosity Shop, made famous by Charles Dickens' book of the same name.

At the end of Portsmouth Street, veer to the left and turn right into John Watkins Plaza. And there I am, on the right: can you see me?

We are now right in the middle of the London School of Economics. If it's term time, I can watch the students milling about. Students have come from all over the world to study here.

It's me! The real Baby Tembo!

Are you going to take a photo of me? Shall we have a photo taken together? A little further along is my friend Pedro Penguin. He loves being hugged.

ALL ABOARD!

Here is a map to help you find the bus stop

Well, wave goodbye and on we go, back to Portugal Street and then left to Kingsway.

At Kingsway turn left again to the big, curving road ahead, Aldwych. We're in for a treat now – a bus ride right through the middle of London, to Kensington and to our last, very exciting treasure. But first we have to get to the bus stop. I have written special instructions to help us get there.

BABY TEMBO'S DIRECTIONS TO THE NO. 9 BUS STOP

1. Cross Kingsway at the traffic lights.

2. Cross Aldwych.

3. Turn left along Aldwych, and then...

4. ...turn right into Melbourne Place.

5. Cross Strand at the lights at the end of Melbourne Place.

6. Just to the right is the number 9 bus stop, labelled 'R'. It is opposite a church in the middle of the road, called St Mary le Strand.

I hope you made it here okay

A SPECIAL BUS RIDE

The number 9 bus ride is definitely a Top Treasure, and here's why!

Firstly, we'll see lots of London's famous sights as we travel along.

Secondly, we are getting on the bus right at the beginning of the route, so with luck you'll be able to get the seats upstairs and right at the front for the best possible view.

Thirdly, we ride along the side of three of London's Royal Parks.

This lovely ride will last for about half an hour, and I've written a guide for you, to help you to spot some of the special London sights we'll be passing. Here we go!

Routemaster Buses

From about 1960 until 2003, Routemaster buses were used all over London. They were gradually exchanged for new, accessible and modern buses, but people missed the lovely old buses so much that they were brought back to run one 'heritage' route through the middle of London, the number 15. We may pass one, so keep your eyes open!

Baby Tembo's Guide to our Bus Ride

Tick off the highlights as we pass them

 Trafalgar Square is on our right, with Nelson's Column reaching to the sky.

 Duke of York Column is on our left. 'When he was up he was up' and there he is. But he's still not as high as Nelson.

 St James' Palace is on the left just before we leave Pall Mall. It was built by Henry VIII, and several members of the Royal Family live here now.

 Piccadilly is a famous and elegant road. On our left we pass The Ritz Hotel, then we ride along the side of our first London park, Green Park.

 Hyde Park Corner is where Green Park and Hyde Park meet. The huge archway on the roundabout is called the Wellington Arch, and on its top the Angel of Peace drives a chariot with four horses. This is called a **quadriga**. What could we call a chariot drawn by four elephants?

Our number 9 bus runs down Knightsbridge, along the edge of Hyde Park. After Knightsbridge Station it skirts our third lovely London park, Kensington Gardens. Look for:

 The Albert Memorial on the right – a huge, richly decorated monument for Queen Victoria's beloved husband (this is the same man who was raising his hat to us at Holborn Circus).

 The Royal Albert Hall opposite the Albert Memorial. Can you see the frieze of pictures around the top of this nearly circular hall?

 Queen's Gate on the right, just past the Albert Memorial; it has beautiful gates with statues of deer and their fawns at each end.

 Kensington Palace which peeps through the trees of Kensington Gardens.

KENSINGTON ROOF GARDENS

We've nearly reached our last treasure.

When you hear the bus announcer say, 'Kensington Palace', then you know that our stop, 'High Street Kensington Station', is next. So give your legs a shake, pick up your bags, and off we go.

We need to turn left off the bus, and then turn right down Derry Street. Number 99 is on the right and we're going inside. The people there are very friendly. We need to go to the desk, and ask to see the garden. Everyone will have to sign the book, and then a posh lift will whisk us up to the roof.

At the top jump out, and WOW! It's a beautiful garden in the sky! There are trees and ponds, a bridge and statues,

beautiful plants and flowers, ducks and even flamingos!

The roofs of other buildings and a big church spire peek in at the edges. There are 'windows' to look out over London, and plenty of seats. It's easy to forget that we are six floors up.

Let's take our time, and enjoy this AMAZING hidden **Top Treasure**.

Here's a picture of me trying to stand

Rest-your-legs page

You can draw people in the windows and put an advertisement along the side.

HYDE PARK CORNER
PICCADILLY CIRCUS
TRAFALGAR SQ.

Have a competition to see who can stand on one leg for the longest time.

amingo; it's harder than it looks!

How many words can you make out of BABY TEMBO?

....

....

....

....

....

....

My **Top Treasure** here? The flamingos, of course!

Kensington Roof Gardens is the largest roof garden in Europe. In the 1930s, this building was a department store called Derry & Toms.

Its chairman, Trevor Bowen, had the idea for 'a garden in the sky' and there is a plaque to remember him on a wall up here. I wonder if you can find it.

Today the gardens are 'Grade Two Listed'. This means that they mustn't be spoiled or destroyed. Sir Richard Branson owns them now, and he kindly allows us to come and see this beautiful place for free.

There are three themed areas:

A Spanish Garden with fountains, covered walkways, pink walls and bright, bright flowers

A Tudor-style garden with archways and secret corners. In summer it is filled with roses and lavender, and smells beautiful! In winter it may be covered with a marquee

An English woodland garden, with over 100 trees! There are 30 different types of tree, and some of them have been here for over 60 years. They seem happy, even though they only have one metre of soil to grow in. There is also a pretty stream (a stream! On a roof! My goodness!) and a pond that is home to all sorts of ducks and four flamingos. Sometimes, when no-one is looking, I suck up water with my trunk and give the birds a lovely shower

When it's time to go, we'll go down in the lift, sign out in the book, and walk back to High Street Kensington Station. And this is where I have to leave you.

I hope you've enjoyed our day together; I certainly have! And I hope you'll come and visit me again one day.

JUST IN CASE...

Occasionally, the Roof Gardens are closed for a private function. If they are, then here's an alternative plan.

Stay on the bus to the other end of Kensington High Street. Get off at the 'Kensington High Street, Earls Court' stop, and visit Holland Park instead. The gates are near the Design Museum. At first it looks like a normal park, but cross the field to the building at the back and there is:

- A lovely area with a big adventure playground
- Woodland walks
- Formal Gardens
- The remains of an old stately home
- A bronze sundial with two life-size giant tortoises
- A nature play area
- Live peacocks
- A Japanese garden
- Plenty of things for you to see and lots of room for elephants – and you – to RUN AROUND in!

Here is the solution to the word search on page 19. Did you find all the words?

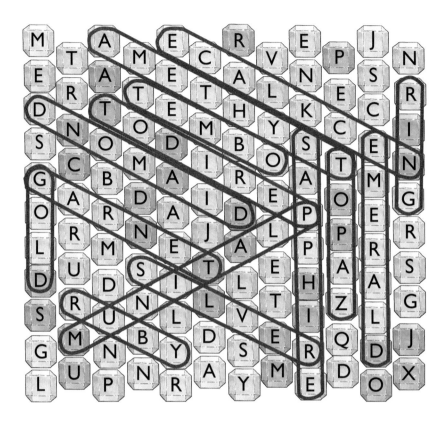

We hope you have enjoyed your day in London with
Step Outside Guides.
If you'd like to let us know what you got up to, or what
extra treasures you found, you can send a message to
feedback@stepoutsideguides.com
If you'd like pictures of your day to be in our online gallery,
send them to
gallery@stepoutsideguides.com

MALE
2 REAL
MAN

THE REAL MAN'S JOURNEY

Book 1

DAVID BURROWS

One Rib Publications
Nassau, The Bahamas

www.oneribpublications.com
oneribpublications@gmail.com

Male to Man: The Real Man's Journey – Book 1
Copyright © 2023 by David Burrows
Published 2023 by One Rib Publications

ISBN: 9 781959 806110

Table of Contents

PREFACE

This book is about a journey. A journey from ignorance to il-lumination, from wandering to purpose. This is a book of re-demption and a book of hope. As a young man growing up, I did not know what a real man was. My ignorance took me down a path of turmoil that almost ended with me being imprisoned, facing substance abuse issues, even losing my life. One fateful day, everything changed, and I embarked on a new journey that led me to an understanding of my original design and purpose, culminating in me becoming a REAL MAN. Welcome to book one of *Male to Man: The Real Man's Journey.*

1 | LOST AND FOUND

My journey is complex and full of paradoxes. I say "is" because I'm still on it. I was not born in the ghetto, but, unfortunately, the ghetto was born in me. I was born into an upper-middle-class Black family in The Bahamas. My father was a self-made businessman who rose from nothing to become a major player in the grocery business. I recall a conversation I had with the major player in the grocery business in The Bahamas, Rupert Roberts, when I worked as the personnel manager for his grocery chain. My father had moved to his native island of Eleuthera and asked me to speak with Mr. Roberts about taking some farm produce that he was growing in Governors Harbour, a major settlement on Eleuthera. When I mentioned my father's name, Mr. Roberts said, "Your father is plenty man." This is a statement of respect; in The Bahamas, if you are referred to as "plenty man," it means you are formidable, a boss, someone to be reckoned with.

I grew up with a "plenty man" father who was formidable in business, but he was not formidable in the home. Like many men in The Bahamas, he had a weakness and a wandering eye for pretty women, and this pursuit contributed to him losing focus on his home. My three sisters managed to stay on the straight and narrow; the boys, however, were a different story. My mother was a strong Christian woman and had us all in church at an early age. The girls remained faithful to the call while the boys went in another direction. My father did not go to church much, and when he did, he went alone. He sent us to church with our mother, and many Sundays you could find him in our backyard sitting on the wall and drinking beer after beer as he watched us pack into the car and drive off to church with mother.

My father and I had a good relationship at first and I looked up to him as a young boy. As I got older, we drifted apart and I started heading in the wrong direction. The streets and the hoods came a calling, and I answered. My older brother "Chimmy" was the first in our family to hit the streets. He became a major player on the streets and was connected to just about every major gangster in The Bahamas, and I followed him. I connected with a crew he created called "the University of Warren Street." In truth, it was a university, a place of higher learning in criminal enterprise, and Chimmy was the president. In this school we learned economics—"buy low and sell high"— and pharmacology. We were street pharmacists with no license to prescribe and sell our pharmaceutical products of weed, cocaine, hashish, and other psychotropic drugs.

The University of Warren Street was home base, because Chimmy was also connected to the gangsters in "Harlem Nassau" (McQuay Street). Harlem was one of the most feared hoods in The Bahamas. I became connected to Harlem through Chimmy. "Poker" was one of the most feared gangsters in Harlem and I became friends with his younger brother a young man known as "Kentuck," or "Bird," who took me through the ropes of the streets from the age of thirteen. I saw him recently and he reminded me that I was one of his "soldiers" back in those days. The lessons I learned as a young boy attending church were replaced by street lessons taught by the most notorious gangsters in the city. Some of these young men that I looked up to became criminal legends in the country: one was executed for killing a police officer and another led the first prison riot in The Bahamas. My friends were rough and abusive. One beat his wife with a golf club, another threw a concrete block on his girlfriend's head then threw water on her to wake her up then beat her again. I did not have good role models and I learned from them how to be the wrong kind of man.

As I grew on the streets, I took advantage of multiple women. I became increasingly violent. From my early teen years I had multiple girlfriends on a regular basis. I assaulted a teacher. I pulled a machete on my father. I struck a young man with a piece of tree limb then hit him in the back of his neck with a big rock. I almost lost my life when the young man returned and chased me through the bushes with a shotgun.

I began clubbing from the age of fourteen with women in their twenties, some of whom were even married. My street professors schooled me in the art of using women. One day, one of my mentors opened a can of grape soda and began to drink it. As he drank, he said, "This tastes sweet." He kept drinking until the soda was almost gone. Then he crushed the can and threw it away. He turned to me and said, "This is how you deal with women—take all the sweetness, and when you are done, move on to the next one."

My street education taught me to thrive in doing wrong. I lied, cheated, stole, robbed, and hustled on the streets, and all the while I thought I was being a real man because the streets told me those were the marks of a real man. Soft men had one girlfriend or wife. Soft men looked for a regular job. Soft men went to church. I was not a soft guy, so I embraced the streets. I had natural intelligence and book smarts, yet I was failing in school because my allegiance was to the streets. Even when I later got a job in a bank, I reverted to my street ways and did things in the bank that would not be good for me to speak about now. When I eventually went to college, I did not change my ways. I was not the influenced, I was the influencer. I messed up my first years of college by doing the same things I used to do on the streets. My friend and I ended up being wanted by the police for some of the things we did involving a handgun and for inventory we acquired without money. Thankfully, the sheriff and the dean of the school in Madison, Florida, gave us a deal, which meant we did not do any time and our records would be clean.

It was at this time that my sister was attending a Christian university and suggested that I join her. I eventually did and it became a turning point in my life. Up to this time the only males I hung around were guys from the streets. My role models were still gangsters, drug dealers and nefarious men. I was lost because the men who were giving me direction were lost themselves. Like the saying goes: When the blind lead the blind, they both fall into a ditch.[1] Many of these men ended up in prison, on drugs, or living lives destroyed by unfruitful and unproductive activities.

My turnaround began when I met my brother-in-law the late Robyn Gool, who was from Detroit but would end up establishing a major ministry in Charlotte, North Carolina, called Victory Christian Center. Robyn and I had nothing in common

---

1   Matthew 15:14.

when we first met. I did not know how I could relate to him. He did not drink. He did not smoke. He did not go to clubs. He did not party. So what was there to relate to? The answer came through our mutual love of basketball. He was a baller and I was a baller; so we connected around basketball.

Almost every day we played ball, in local gyms, parks, anywhere we could. Sometimes it was in the hood and sometimes it was at a local college gym. He was competitive, liked to win, so we went at it day after day. After balling, we would stop by the donut shop and get some donuts; he liked milk with his and I liked apple juice with mine. Not only did we play ball, but we also watched games together on a regular basis, NBA, NFL, College football and Basketball, just about any major sporting event. Through this bond we began to talk about other issues. He asked me questions about the future, and most of the time I had no answer. I started going with him to Bible study. I had not been to church since I was eleven, so church was strange to me, and the Bible studies were stranger still.

When I was growing up, being in church was for women, old people, and people who did not know how to have fun. But the people in Robyn's Bible study seemed so happy; they talked about blessings and God giving us favor. I listened as people gave testimonies of the goodness of God and how their lives were changed, and I became more curious. As I spent more time with Robyn, I became really impressed with how he lived. He was a strong Black man who was faithful to his wife, and his life was in stark contrast to mine. I began to realize that I needed to change my course, and eventually, I made that change.

That change began a slow revolution in my life, especially as it related to relationships with women. I stopped having indiscriminate sex. I stopped cursing, stopped drugs and alcohol and I began the journey to becoming a law-abiding, productive citizen focused on helping others. In many ways, I experienced a reeducation in what a man is. This led me to have more stable relationships and, eventually, to my marriage and faithfulness to my wife. Many of my friends could not believe my transformation. I became a family man, taking care of my children and becoming a role model.

I returned home to The Bahamas after college and began speaking in schools and churches and many young men also changed their lives because of my testimony. Soon I was leading a movement that focused on gangs and which saw over a thousand gang members make commitments to Christ in one year, with many of them making the transition from criminal and abuser to role-model citizen and father.

This journey from *Male to Man* **is not theory or speculation**; this is a real-life experience and principles that have worked to change, first, my life and then the lives of countless others I have had the pleasure of working with. I experienced my transformation without having full knowledge of the principles behind it. I learned from a variety of men and through biblical principles what I believe represents the foundation of a great life, the foundation of what it means to be a REAL MAN.

What follows in each chapter are those principles. I am sharing them because I realize I am not alone on this journey. There is a global epidemic of misguided and lost men, and the potential consequences of this trend are serious. The greatest problem in the world today is the lost or missing man. Consider these statistics:

- Fathers play an important role in a child's development and can affect a child's social competence, performance in school, and emotion regulation.

- Fathers can also affect a child's well-being indirectly. A supportive relationship between parents is linked to better self-regulation in a child.[2]

- In the United States one in four Black males has been to prison or is in prison or on probation.

- The leading cause of death among Black males ages 13 to 35 years is homicide (normally by another Black male).

- Over 70% of households in inner-city communities are headed by a single female.

- Over 93% of prison inmates are males.

- 75% of inmates are between the ages of 25 and 35 years old.

- 70% of men have been unfaithful to their wives at some point.

- 39% of men who call themselves Christian have been unfaithful in their marriage.[3]

Males, young and old, need to understand, know, and become REAL MEN. Real men are

Ready **E**ager **A**ggressive **L**eaders
Redeemed **E**xcellent **A**spirational **L**eaders

If you want to become a real man, the journey begins here.

---

2   PSYCHOLOGY TODAY
3   Statistics from the Barna research group and the US Department of Justice

2 | WHO AND WHAT IS A MAN?

Let's begin with a few questions.

Is a male the same as a man?

Is man a physical being or spiritual being? Or a combination of physical and spiritual?

Why do men cheat?

Why do men fight?

Why do men compete?

"Animals risk their lives for food, men risk their lives for acceptance."[4] The Bible tells us that man was God's idea. It was God who said let us make man.[5] When He said "make man," God could not have been referring to making a spirit because the Scripture also says that God breathed into man His spirit, which gave life to man's body.[6] Therefore man is made from the dirt, but his spirit does not come from the dirt. His spirit comes from

---

4   Anonymous.
5   Genesis 1:26.
6   Genesis 2:7.

God and lives within a physical house (which is later referred to in the Bible as a tent, or temporary structure). So, man is a physical being with a spirit. Man also has what is called a soul, which consists of the mind, will and emotions.

God created two versions of the species man, one called male and the other called female. When we speak of man on earth, we are usually referring to a physical structure that houses a male. The male is someone who has the characteristics of a male, namely, a physique, or structure, with naturally pronounced muscles, facial hair, a penis, and hormones predominated by testosterone which usually makes a man both strong and aggressive.

The female is characterized by the presence of a womb (which gives her the ability to carry and birth children), breasts that bear milk, and a vagina which is a receptive organ designed to receive the male in order to produce children. The man (male) possesses male anatomy and characteristics and the female—(woman) possesses female anatomy and characteristics.

Your housing determines your function; that is, if you have a female house, you are supposed to function as a female. If you have a male house, you are supposed to function as a male. It is well documented that many people have dysphorias [some people do have gender dysphoria] where they perceive themselves as something [being a sex] other than who [the one at birth] they are. But this is a mental disorder and not a reality. I have no intention of addressing or debating this issue as there is nothing for me to debate and I possess no confusion or misunderstanding about what or who is a male.

God is the source and sustainer of man. The survival of anything or anyone on earth is usually tied to its source and natural environment. For example: fish thrive when connected to water, plants thrive when connected to soil, and man thrives when connected to God. A fish may live briefly out of water, but it cannot thrive because nothing thrives outside its source and natural environment.

The *male* is a physical being, but *man* is the spirit that lives inside the physical being. You could say, then, that the male is the house and the man is the occupant of the house. Man is a spirit being made after the image and likeness of God. Therefore, man encompasses both male and female from a spiritual perspective. Jesus said God is Spirit and those who want to worship Him (connect with Him) must do so in spirit.[7]

Since man is a spirit, when he is not connected to God his source, he is reduced to being a male without life from his source. Without connection to God, man operates on instinct, like the fish and the bird. A dog operates entirely on instinct and is very predictable. If he sees another female dog, he will go after it looking for sex. He does not calculate risks or think about who is going to provide for children that may come out of the sexual encounter. A man who is operating only in the flesh acts the same way: he seeks only to fulfill his fleshly desires. Perhaps it is coincidental that we live in a world where men refer to themselves as "dogs"— Nate Dogg, Snoop Dog, Bow Wow, Pitbull. We were made in the image of God, but we are conforming to the image of a dog instead.

---

7   John 4:24.

The natural man and the spirit man are different, as these scriptures show:

1 Corinthians 2:14

> But the natural man does not receive the things of the Spirit of God, for they are foolishness to him; nor can he know them, because they are spiritually discerned. NKJV

Romans 8:5–10

> For those who live according to the flesh set their minds on the things of the flesh, but those who live according to the Spirit, the things of the Spirit. For to be carnally minded is death, but to be spiritually minded is life and peace. Because the carnal mind is enmity against God; for it is not subject to the law of God, nor indeed can be. So then, those who are in the flesh cannot please God.

> But you are not in the flesh but in the Spirit, if indeed the Spirit of God dwells in you. Now if anyone does not have the Spirit of Christ, he is not His. And if Christ is in you, the body is dead because of sin, but the Spirit is life because of righteousness. NKJV

The man who is operating in the spirit acts differently from the man who is operating in the flesh. When a man meets and is connected to God, he no longer operates just (purely) on physical instincts but according to the spiritual instructions that supersede physical instincts and desires. The primary motivation of a male is sex (flesh). Have you ever noticed that no matter how educated a man is, no matter his occupation or position, if he is not connected to God he pursues sex. We have heard of prime ministers, presidents, CEOs, pastors, and other professionals who have lost their marriages, careers, even ended up in prison, because of their pursuit of sex.

I too have lived the "dog life." I had to learn that love is not sex. I also had to relearn sex according to God's purpose and design. Sex is not love. Sex can be an expression of Love in a relationship but it is not love in itself. If sex were love then the most loved people in the world would be prostitutes. Most men are caught in a system which has programmed men to approach life with one or all of the following mindsets:

VCU (Vagina-centered universe) — Here, men spend all their lives figuring out how to get more vaginas. They will conspire, beg, borrow, steal, and do whatever they have to do to get more, even if they are legally married and can get what they need at home.

GSM (Game, sport, macho competition) — The motivation is to be the biggest, strongest, fastest. These men are in a continual contest and competition about sports, male strength, physical prowess. They play sports, have played sports, or are sports team fanatics. If not competing over sports, GSM men compete over cards, dice, anything to test who is the strongest or best.

FOI (Fellowship of the intoxicated) — These men hang out in bars or on the corner, get high and drunk all the time and do nothing particularly useful. They will play dominoes, watch games, or just sit and talk about mostly irrelevant things while they down beers or smoke joints.

For most men there is no intentional education and there are few positive role models in God-centered manhood (the original); so, to become real men, **re-education is necessary.**

If you understand how you were designed, you can also understand what your purpose is and how you should function on the earth. I was one of the males who pursued sex until I connected to God, and since that time satisfying my flesh—sex, women, and fleshly pursuits—has become secondary rather than primary.

These lyrics from a popular 1980s funk song sum up the struggle of the man living without God: he will chase the **cat** all the days of his life.

> Why must I feel like that
> Oh, why must I chase the cat
>
> Nothing but the Dog in me
>
> Like the boys
> When they're out there walkin' the streets
> May compete
> Nothin' but the dog in ya
>
> Bow-wow-wow-yippie-yo-yippie-yeah
> Bow-wow-yippie-yo-yippie-yeah
> Bow-wow-wow-yippie-yo-yippie-yeah
> Bow-wow-yippie-yo-yippie-yeah

The man who is spiritually connected learns to function in his role and not just chase the cat. Many men who are reading this book were or are chasers of the cat. The first key to success as a man is learning your purpose and design; then everything else in your life can line up. Here is how the Bible describes the man who is connected to God:

Blessed is the man who fears the Lord,
Who delights greatly in His commandments.

His descendants will be mighty on earth;
The generation of the upright will be blessed.
Wealth and riches will be in his house,
And his righteousness endures forever.
Unto the upright there arises light in the darkness;
He is gracious, and full of compassion, and righteous.

—Psalm 112:1b–4 nkjv (emphasis added by author)

As men, we are actually triune beings like God: we are spirit first, soul second, and body third. The biggest problem for the man occurs because he doesn't understand the proper order of his existence and operates in reverse order, with the body being preeminent.

Man actually [truly] needs a relationship with God to maximize his potential in the earth. Man must learn to worship God in spirit and in truth; he must get to know God's Word and the principles we are supposed to live by. If a man does not get this information, he will essentially walk around in darkness and operate outside his purpose.

This is God's description of the man who operates outside of Him:

God stands in the congregation of the mighty;
He judges among the gods.
How long will you judge unjustly,
And show partiality to the wicked? Selah

Defend the poor and fatherless;
Do justice to the afflicted and needy.
Deliver the poor and needy;
Free them from the hand of the wicked.

They do not know, nor do they understand;
They walk about in darkness;
All the foundations of the earth are unstable.

I said, "You are gods,
And all of you are children of the Most High.
But you shall die like men,
And fall like one of the princes."

—Psalm 82:1–7 NKJV

3 | KNOW YOUR ROLE

Our world today is often driven by body and soul and not spirit. This disorder creates confusion, because man was designed to operate as spirit first, then soul, and then body. If a man is run [guided] by his body, he will destroy himself. For example, if we follow our body's desire for food, we may not eat what is good for us and thereby become overweight or develop noncommunicable lifestyle diseases, such as hypertension and diabetes. If we follow our body's desire for sex, we may engage in indiscriminate sex resulting in unwanted [unplanned] pregnancies, sexually transmitted diseases (STD), damaged children (lacking love, affection, and abused) and broken societies. The only way to control oneself is to look beyond the body for instructions and guidance. The Bible puts it this way: "*For to be carnally minded* [focused on flesh] *is death, but to be spiritually minded* [focused on God] *is life and peace*" (Romans 8:6 nkjv Emphasis added by author). We have to focus on our spirit to master our flesh; this mastery is called self-control.

Let's look at the role of man as outlined by God Himself.

Role #1 FATHER

Man is born with the capacity to father. In some cases, he may never become a father, but he is born with the capacity. Capacity indicates role. A man has no capacity to mother; so being a woman or mother is not his role. Noted pastor and author Myles Munroe taught that "Wherever purpose is not known, abuse—abnormal use—is inevitable." Man needs to know his role, otherwise he will abuse himself and abuse those who are under his care or authority. Even if you never father a child physically, you are born with the capacity to father, and understanding this role helps you to prepare for life ahead with clarity and confidence.

Role #2 GIVER

Man was not designed to be a receiver; therefore, receiver is not his natural role. If he becomes a receiver, he is operating outside of normal use. The organ he possesses, called the penis, was designed for a corresponding receptacle on the woman, called a vagina. This is very obvious from a natural perspective. There are men who have a psychological defect that causes them to perceive themselves as receivers; but this perception is contrary to the original design, and to normalcy, in my opinion. It is clear to me that a receiving man is an aberration, an abnormality.

Man is designed to be a giver; he is designed to be a father; he is designed to be stronger than a woman physically. This physical strength is a natural fact. No matter what is in a man's mind, he will never have a "period" and he will never have a "womb" and he will never bear children or breastfeed his children. The male man has a specific role that is different from the female.

Role #3 LEADER OF FAMILY

The Bible is specific about the role of the man: "*Therefore a man shall leave his father and mother* [specifically] *and be joined to his wife, and they shall become one flesh*" (Genesis 2:24 Emphasis added by author). This scripture tells us that the role of a man is to leave his father and mother and start his own family. The Bible refers to the husband as the head of the home. Eph 5.23 states, "For the husband is head of the wife, as also Christ is head of the church; and He is the Savior of the body". He is head not necessarily because he is smarter or more qualified than the woman, but because God designed the family to be headed by the husband (Ephesians 5:22–24). How this plays out in real life is dynamic, but the principle is real.

Role #4 FOUNDATION OF SOCIETY

Not only is the man designed as head of his family, but he is also the foundation of society. Statistics indicate that when men are not in the home, the societies around them begin to fail. The suicide rate among teens goes up by 95 percent, drug abuse among teens goes up, imprisonment of teens goes up according to several studies. When the foundation is not solid, the building will develop structural problems and will crumble over time.

The man is the anchor of the family. A family that is built on a single mother can function well and, through tremendous resilience, the mother can make up for the loss of the father. But the consequences of this are like having a one-wheel bicycle: the single mother can become so proficient at operating on one wheel that she, her children, and society forget what a difference the second wheel makes. Men and women are needed in the home because of family design.

Role #5 PHYSICALLY STRONGER PARTNER

A man is naturally stronger than a woman. The presence of the hormone testosterone dictates that a man can run faster, jump higher, and lift more weight than a woman of equal size. Some women are stronger than men, but they are not the norm. This natural difference in physical strength is evident in sports. Serena Williams, who at one time was the greatest [highest ranked female tennis player in the world] and is still considered among the greatest if not the greatest female players of all time, when asked how she would fare in the men's game indicated that a male player ranked in the top 200 could easily defeat her. The difference in physical strength is a good reason [also helps us to understand that] the woman was not designed to fight. Men were chosen for battle not because of discrimination but because of obvious [naturally present] facts about their superior physical strength.

Role #6 MORE LOGICAL THAN EMOTIONAL PARTNER

Women are usually much more detail-oriented than men. If you ask a woman a question, she likely will go back years and include numerous details in her answer, whereas a man would tend to give a short one- or two-word answer. I remember returning from a funeral and my wife asking me how it was. I replied that everything was fine, it was a typical funeral. She asked if she had done something to offend me. What I had forgotten was that when my wife asks how the funeral was, what she means is, "Who was there? What were they wearing? Who sang in the choir? Were the family emotional or calm? Did the pastor preach a good sermon?" But I had answered her in a typically male way—with just a few words. I realized then that the next time I go to a funeral,

I need to observe and take notes so I can give her a more woman friendly answer and with details.

Role #7 PROVIDER AND PROTECTOR

Today men and women share equal space in the workplace. Many women are the providers in their family. This role is by necessity and not by design. I do not have a problem with women as providers because of the realities of the day, but this role change of necessity is not [should not replace the] original design. The word father means "source and sustainer"; so the man is destined to provide for his family. Lack of knowledge of this role has caused the man to be derelict in his duty and has thrust the woman into a role that should not be hers.

The woman can [and may] work, and in many fields she is equal to the man. The original design of the woman is to be primary nurturer and caregiver. Her purpose is indicated in her design, and she is not primarily designed for work. She is wired for nurturing. The woman is equal to the man intellectually and can operate on the same or higher level in many environments. There is nothing wrong with a woman being a leader or executive. Notwithstanding these attributes, the woman is designed, wired, to be the primary nurturer and caregiver in the family. Only she can birth a baby and, since the man has no breast milk, she is the baby's primary nurturer.

There was a time when my wife worked as an insurance executive, a Vice President in a multinational firm, she earned much more than I did, had a company car, bonuses and carried much of the financial load of the family. We did not consider it an issue because we did not have two families, each of us contributed to one family financial pool for the benefit of the entire family.

There was not need to point fingers or for me to feel guilty, I did my best and she did her best and together we provided for our family. A man should do his best to provide and the wife is there to support him and the family as needed.

The man possesses physical strength and a disposition that makes him a natural protector. He is designed both to provide for and to protect his family. The Bible states that if a man does not work, he should not eat.[8] **2 Thessalonians 3.10 "For even when we were with you, this we commanded you, that if any would not work, neither should he eat".** This means that the man is supposed to be productive. He can work year-round: he does not have "periods" and does not have to give birth or breastfeed; so it is easier for him to be in the workplace and function as provider. A man is built for work.

Role #8 THE MASCULINE PARTNER

The natural design of the man is for him to be masculine. The predominant hormone of the man is testosterone, which designs him to be masculine. Men have physical strength and are naturally competitive because of their physicality and masculinity. Men tend to be physically aggressive and pursuit-oriented. If you put two women in a room, they will size up one another based upon looks, makeup, fashion, and other feminine things. If you put two men in a room, they tend to default to competition around strength—Who is the strongest? Who can run the fastest? There are men who may be more feminine than masculine, but the original and natural design is for a man to be masculine.

---

8   2 Thessalonians 3:10.

Men and women are different by design and purpose. The purpose of muscles and testosterone is to support strength activities complementing the man's naturally masculine status. Women possess the hormone estrogen and are inclined naturally to be feminine. Estrogen is what causes a woman to have menstrual periods and a female personality and makeup [structure]. Men and women are not interchangeable; they are distinct in design and purpose. The man is stimulated by sight and tends to be a hunter both in nature and in relationships. The woman and the man are equal in intellect but not in physical strength. Women cannot do many things a man can do, and a man cannot do many things a woman can do. Knowing your role makes it easier to function. Apostle John stated in one of his letters that he was writing to "young men because you are strong,"[9] meaning, men are uniquely equipped for their role.

---

9   1 John 2:14.

4 | FIND YOUR PURPOSE

The key to life is purpose. If you know your purpose, your life is easier. Purpose is the key to fulfillment. Where purpose is not known, abuse is the inevitable result. If you do not know the purpose for milk and out of ignorance you put it in a car, that abnormal use of milk will cause malfunction of the car. The man who knows his purpose is a man who is aligned with his natural function and can thrive. To discover the purpose of the man, we have to look at what God gave the man.

God-Given Attributes of the Man

1. Image

"Image" means to look like. We look like God, and likeness indicates function. We are supposed to look and act like God. He gave us His image to represent, or re-present, Him in the earth. "Re" means to do again, and "present" means to display visibly. The man is supposed to be the image and likeness of God on earth causing people to see God and be drawn to Him because of our reflection of Him. Men often do not know that God gave them His image and likeness for a purpose; so, instead of acting like GOD, we act more like DOG. We even call ourselves dogs as a term of endearment. The dog cannot represent God: a dog has no conscience; a dog acts on his physical and sexual instincts; a dog does not know how to reason. Dogs do not maintain families or communities; they simply carry out their instinctive functions based upon their physical makeup. You, on the other hand, are made in GOD'S IMAGE. You come with a design, a purpose and function. Your assignment is to be a reflection of God. Jesus was referred to as the image of God in the flesh, meaning this is the example of how men are to function.

2. Presence

God gave the man His Spirit to live in him. No other animal lives in the presence of God. In the garden of Eden, the man fellowshipped with and talked with God. God gave the man dominion and authority over all other creatures as His representative in the earth. People say the lion is the king of the jungle, but the lion can never be king over the man because the man was given dominion over the animals. If you put the man in the jungle, he would figure out a way to subdue the lion; but if you put a lion in a village, he would not figure out how to conquer the man, except for an initial encounter based upon physical attributes. The presence of God in the man enables him to hear from and communicate with God and use His presence to change his environment. When the man is connected to God and has His presence, he becomes a man of purpose. Outside of God, we are just dirt; with God, we are living dirt with a purpose. Just like a fish needs water, or a plant needs soil, the man needs God. Without God, the man is both disconnected and lost and will self-destruct. The presence of God is where the man receives life; therefore, men must live in the presence of God. This is the reason men need to know how to worship, pray and experience the presence of God.

3. Assignment

The man was designed to work. After the presence of God, the next thing the man needs—even before he needs a woman or children—is work. God gave man work as the first and most important assignment after His presence. The man was designed to work and be productive. Anytime a man does not work, he tends to drift and get lost. An idle man is a dangerous man. I have found in my work with young people that productive young men are the easiest to work with. Work represents value; a man without work feels undervalued. If he is working and productive, he will get in less trouble and is less likely to abuse substances. Work represents dignity, and without work a man becomes aimless.

The woman was not designed to work in the same way that the man was designed to work. A woman can work, and work effectively; but "can do" and "designed to do" are different things. The creation story of Genesis explains that "*before any plant of the field was in the earth and before any herb of the field had grown. For the Lord God had not caused it to rain on the earth, and there was no man to till the ground,*"[10] and **before God gave the man the woman, He gave the man work.** The man is designed to work, to fulfill his assignment, to release his gift. Work can be a job or it can be a business. But even if a man is not being paid, he should work, because nonproductivity is one of the worst curses of the man. Remember this, real men: If no job is available, create one or work for free until a paying job becomes available. I have seen

---

10   Genesis 2:5.

many young men to whom I gave this advice end up in lucrative jobs because they went to work in their field of interest and when a vacancy became available, they were picked because they were available [present].

4. Territory

The reason the Bible tells the man to leave his mother and father is that each man should have a territory to rule over. In order to rule effectively, one must learn to manage a domain, a territory. Every man should have a domain that he oversees. A man needs a place that is his own. If he is to have a wife and a family, he needs to have his own territory. Even if he has only an apartment, he needs a place that he provides for and leads. If we look at God's instructions in the beginning, the man was given the earth as his **domain** and instructed to subdue, control, and produce. Every man needs a domain.

5. Dominion

The Bible tells us that the man was given dominion, meaning, he was given the right to rule over a territory and everything in it. God created the man and gave him the right to rule. The man is supposed to dominate his environment by making the most of the resources. He was told to subdue everything under his domain: to control plants, birds, animals, and everything in the environment for his benefit. **He was never given dominion over the woman or other men**, His job is to protect his environment and ensure that it is replenished so that resources never run out. Everything for earth is already on earth and has been from the beginning.

The principle of seedtime and harvest means that we will never run out of resources as long as we take care of what God gave us as he designed. Seeds will always produce trees which will produce fruit which produce seeds that become trees that produce fruit. The man was told to dominate everything on earth except other men and women. The problem in the world today is that the man is being dominated by plants and herbs, instead of the other way around. Alcohol comes from plants, cocaine is a plant, and now the man is being dominated by plants instead of dominating the plants for his benefit. The man gave names to the animals and he called the woman, woman. Man and woman were both given dominion, but the man was given primary dominion in a family, with the wife serving as his equal assistant. Apostle Paul counsels the men of the church at Ephesus to love their wives, but he does not tell the woman to love her husband; instead, he counsels the women to respect their husband. This means the woman is to acknowledge her husband and allow him to exercise his dominion in partnership with her. The man is not a dictator over the woman; they are supposed to be a team functioning according to purpose and design.

6. Responsibility

The man was given responsibility for territory and for family. When God approached Abraham, he said he chose Abraham because he would teach and direct his children.[11] Man was given responsibility for his wife and children. He doesn't have to be the smartest or the best at anything, he just needs to know that it is his responsibility to protect, provide, teach, love and direct his household. When men abdicate or shun their responsibility, the

11 Genesis 18:19.

family disintegrates, the community disintegrates, and, eventually, the world disintegrates.

The number-one problem in the world today is the lack of responsibility of men. An irresponsible man causes his wife to have to do double duty and perform in roles she was not designed to perform in alone. A woman can succeed without a man present in the home, but the job is much harder and the success rate much lower. Men need to be responsible. Too many men today are in prison and nonproductive. The man is responsible for teaching his children the ways of God. The primary learning source for children is not supposed to be the school or the church; it is supposed to be the home. If the man is not connected to God, he cannot teach his children right from wrong and instruct them in the ways of God, which God Himself instructed the man to teach.

7. Authority

Every army has a chain of command, or authority. There are generals, commanders, captains, sergeants, all the way down to privates and recruits. During times of war, the chain of command runs from the top to the bottom. God designed an authority structure and in the home the man is the general. He is not a ruling general; he is a servant general. His authority is legitimized to the extent that he is submitted to God's rulership. One day, Jesus encountered a centurion, a commander of a hundred soldiers. The centurion asked Jesus to heal his servant and Jesus said to him, "'I will come and heal him.'" But the centurion said to Jesus, You do not have to come; just give Your word, I know Your word is good enough to make it happen. The centurion explained that he too was in a position of authority and his soldiers act upon his word. Jesus replied that this was the greatest example of faith he had seen.[12] The man needs to be in position and function in his God-given authority. When he is not where he is supposed to be, the chain of command is broken and the family is broken. Psalm 112 outlines how a man functioning in his purpose—called a "good man"—impacts life:

A good man deals graciously and lends;
He will guide his affairs with discretion.
Surely he will never be shaken;
The righteous will be in everlasting remembrance.
He will not be afraid of evil tidings;
His heart is steadfast, trusting in the Lord.
His heart is established;
He will not be afraid,
Until he sees his desire upon his enemies.

He has dispersed abroad,
He has given to the poor;
His righteousness endures forever;
His horn will be exalted with honor.
The wicked will see it and be grieved;
He will gnash his teeth and melt away;
The desire of the wicked shall perish.

8. *Father*

The purpose of the man is to father. He has the capacity to father biologically. Having biological children is vital, but having non biological children is just as important. I have only one biological son, but I have fathered hundreds, perhaps even thousands,

---

12   Matthew 8:5–13.

of men. Biological fatherhood is only one aspect of fatherhood. Men need a model of what a man is. Many of the young men I have had the pleasure of working with looked to me as a role model. They learned how to be men because I gave them the image of what a man and a father should be. Today many of these men—who came from abusive environments, were gang members or criminals—are family men and fathers, unlike their own biological parents and siblings. Many of these men have testified publicly that they consider me to be their father and that if they had to depend on their biological father, they would be lost. The father is so important [essential] to individual and social stability. Social science has proved that things fall apart when men are not in their proper role:

- 90% of all homeless and runaway children are from fatherless homes – 32 times the national average.

- 71% of all high school dropouts come from fatherless homes – 9 times the national average. (National Principals Association Report)

- 75% of all adolescent patients in chemical abuse centers come from fatherless homes – 10 times the national average.

- 63% of youth suicides are from fatherless homes (U.S. Department of Health/Census) – 5 times the national average.

- 70% of youths in state-operated institutions come from fatherless homes – 9 times the national average. (U.S. Department of Justice)

- 85% of all youths in prison come from fatherless homes – 20 times the national average.

(Fulton County, Georgia and Texas Department of Corrections)

- Children of single-parent homes are more than twice as likely to commit suicide.

- 85% of all children who show behavior disorders come from fatherless homes – 20 times the national average. (Centers for Disease Control and Prevention)

- 80% of rapists with anger problems come from fatherless homes –14 times the national average. ("The Developmental Antecedents and Adult Adaptations of Rapist Subtypes." *Criminal Justice and Behavior*, Volume 14 Issue 4, December 1987, pp. 403-426)

Fatherhood is crucial!

5 | THE REAL MAN'S JOURNEY

A REAL MAN IS SEVERAL THINGS:

Strong in character
Committed to the family
Committed to social responsibilities
Morally strong
Physically disciplined,
Spiritually mature
Dedicated to mentoring others

2 JOURNEYS

The Two main life journeys that all males are born with the potential to navigate effectively are:

1. o Son to Man to Husband to Father
2. o Follower to Leader to Agent of Change

3 RELATIONSHIP

Three types of relationships that are necessary to effectively navigate these journeys

1. o Up Reach – to relate with that which is considered greater than you

2. o In Reach – to expose and develop that which is in you

3. o Out Reach – to influence that which is outside of you

5 PASSIONS

Five passions that can create success for men or derail the two male life journeys if managed ineffectively

1. **Worship** - This related to a mans relationship with God. If this is missing or ineffective a man lacks moral judement, fidelity, spiritual insight and exixts for mainly carnal self seeking purposes. He is unlikely to have a stable family and is not a stable husband or role model. Men will Worship someone or something and will have Heroes, Mentors, Protectors and Providers. If he learns to turn to God and worship him he will find himself. If he worships the wrong heroes and has the wrong mentors the end result is idle and IDOL worship with no good outcome.

2. **Wisdom** - Knowledge can come from books but Wisdom comes from God himself. Knowledge does not translate to wisdom. A doctor may be aware that smoking is not good for the lungs but lacking in wisdom (knowing what to do with knowledge) he smokes and gets cancer all the while having excellent scientific knowledge of the subject. Many men today have knowledge but lack Wisdom

3. **Winning** - Men are natural competitors. Sports often pays more money that any other vocation because men like to compete or watch competition in the areas of speed, strength and skill. Men like to win or associate with winners. If this is not managed and directed he will spend the rest of his life engaging in or watching competitions and seeking to win. If directed correctly he may still pursue sports but will aslo take this energy to produce a winning family, winning children and a winning community. Winning goes beyond sports into such subject areas as wealth creation, appearance and possessions.

4. **Wealth** - Man will pursue money all the days of his life. There is a noble pursuit of money and there is evil pursuit of money. If he learns to gain money through skill and productivity to use for good he has done well. If he gets caught up in pursuing money for evil purposes and through unproductive and illegal means, money becomes a noose around his neck that could cause him to end up in prison or lose his life. Our jails are full of men who have not learned to manage this passion for money. Wealth includes vocation, productivity, investment and possessions.

5. **Women** - Men were made for women. A normal man will be attracted to women and will pursue relationships with women. How this passion is managed is key to his success or failure and actually holds the key to successful societies. Until a man understands the purpose of Woman and the purpose of relationships he is likely to mismange this passion and it becomes a disruptive factor that leads to pain and misery, broken relationships and dysfunction. If he learns to manage this passion in line with God's design there is great benefit

to both him and the world around him. Men must learn to navigate sexual relations according to original design, establishment of relationships on different levels, companionship and family.

These passions employed as intended, produce men with the ability to positively affect their life and the lives of those within their leadership and influence. Most, if not all males at some point have been driven by these passions in a manner other than was intended, and consequently become victims for a time of these passions. These are normal and natural passions of men that can produce pleasure or pain, benefit or loss, trial or triumph.

6 | DEVELOP YOUR VISION

MEN ARE FINDERS (DISCOVERERS) If a man is to lead, or function, in a leadership role, he needs a vision. How can he ask a woman to follow him and how can she follow him if he does not know where he is going? The Bible tells us that where there is no vision, the people will perish.[13] Likewise a family will perish if the man has no vision. Every man needs a vision that he can share with his family. God tells a man to find a wife[14], and even states that whoever "finds a wife finds a good thing, and obtains favour of the Lord."[15] There is no indication [similar appeal] for a wife to find a husband. Before he finds a wife, a man needs a vision. After he has a vision, he can go and find a wife.

What is a vision? A vision is a photograph or image of a desired future. You should never begin a journey without knowing the destination. In the same way, a man needs to know the destination to which he is taking his family. His wife can help him and refine him, but he needs something for her to help with—a vision. God describes a wife as a helper (the literal word in the King James Version is "helpmeet"), or someone who helps a man

---

13   Proverbs 29:18.
14   Genesis 2:24.
15   Proverbs 18:22.

meet his goals. A wife is designed to complement her husband, not to replace him.

A man needs to find a few things that are a part of his vision.

He must have a vision for his own life first.

He must discover his purpose, understand who he is.

He must determine where he wants to go in life, what he wants to become. If he knows what career or business he wants to engage in, this helps with the vision process.

He should also have a vision for his family. Having a vision for work is great, but he must also have a vision for his family. The vision should not be just in his head, it should be written down, the same way you would have an architectural design of your house before you build it. When you design your house, you are showing what your future home will look like. A man should have a future family design to present to his wife, and when children come along, they should see the blueprint also.

There was a time on my real-man journey when I decided my wife and I needed our own home; we had lived in several apartments. I sat down with my wife and we designed the home we wanted and then began pursuing it. I also had a vision for my family. I knew what I wanted my children to be like. I had a vision of them, first of all, in a relationship with God, then successfully educated and finding a successful career or business, and eventually doing what my wife and I had done, creating their own family. Children are with you not to be with you permanently. The Bible says we are supposed to direct (point) our children in the way they should go.

Another part of the real man's vision for his family is provision.

> A good man leaves an inheritance to his children's children,
> But the wealth of the sinner is stored up for the righteous.
>
> Much food is in the fallow ground of the poor,
> And for lack of justice there is waste.
>
> He who spares his rod hates his son,
> But he who loves him disciplines him promptly.
>
> The righteous eats to the satisfying of his soul,
> But the stomach of the wicked shall be in want.
>
> —Proverbs 13:22–25 nkjv

A good man, or real man, leaves an inheritance and a legacy for his children. When children become successful, they should provide for their own family, and if they are in a position, they should honor their parents with their substance; but parents should not demand children take care of them. A real man positions his children and releases them to their destiny. They in turn may honor him based upon their own convictions.

A vision is a photograph of the future, but the vision needs to become a plan. A plan is the practical steps to achieving the vision. It is critical to write your plans down and develop a strategy to reach your goals. A man must be able to offer something more in life than sperm. Not only must he provide sperm, he must be in place to manage creation, both God's creation and his creation. The reason we have a leaderless generation today is we have had successive generations of fathers who lacked vision. Vision changes the atmosphere; it increases self-confidence. One of the problems with our world today is that we have raised a generation dominated by visionless men. In many of our cities, the young men have no vision, no plan; so, they populate the prisons and the graveyards. A man who has a vision for his life and family will *not* continue in fruitless destructive pursuits, like selling drugs and gangbanging. These are pursuits of the blind. The end is obvious and there is no visible long-term benefit, yet some young men continue on the path and end up released from prison in their forties and fifties, with no house, job or anything to show for their evil pursuits.

I watched several prominent gang members from Los Angeles lament how they were sorry they had wasted their lives and had to start over, with nothing to give their children and no positive legacy. Essentially, we have an almost leaderless, visionless generation. We have leaderless homes and leader-compromised homes where women are forced to attempt to be both father and mother. Women are assuming leadership by default rather than by design. Every man should have a vision and a plan. He should not leave his parents' house without a viable and reasonable plan. If you are a real man, you should have a vision and a plan.

7 | BE AN HONORABLE MAN

What is an honorable man? The honorable man is the ideal man, and the ideal man is the real man. Apostle Paul describes what an honorable man looks like in his first letter to a young man named Timothy.[16] God wants us to be honorable men, not dishonorable men. Our families, our children, our neighborhoods, our country should be proud of who we are. They should not be afraid or run when they see us coming. They should not be able to use such words as "no good," "bum," "crook," "immoral," or "thief" to describe us. **Honor means to respect or esteem highly.** Honorable means someone who can be looked up to and trusted. If you want a picture of what an honorable man looks like, hold yourself up to the mirror Paul set before Timothy and ask yourself, **"Am I worthy to be called an honorable man?"** If you are not, then make this your goal. Let's take a look at what God requires for a man to be called honorable and of good character.

Now the overseer [responsible man] *must be above reproach, the husband of but one wife, temperate, self-controlled, respectable, hospitable, able to teach, not given to drunkenness, not violent but gentle, not quarrelsome, not a lover of*

---

16   1 Timothy 3.

money. He must manage his own family well and see that his children obey him with proper respect. (If anyone does not know how to manage his own family, how can he take care of God's church?) —1 Timothy 3:2–5

These verses refer to persons [men] who want to serve in the church, but they also contain the essential characteristics of the honorable man. To serve in authority before God, a man must be right with God, or righteous, and possess the qualities that are favorable in God's eyes.

Here's another English version of the same verses above:

This is a faithful saying: If a man desires the position of a bishop, he desires a good work. A bishop then must be blameless, the husband of one wife, temperate, sober-minded, of good behavior, hospitable, able to teach; not given to wine, not violent, not greedy for money, but gentle, not quarrelsome, not covetous; one who rules his own house well, having his children in submission with all reverence (for if a man does not know how to rule his own house, how will he take care of the church of God?); not a novice, lest being puffed up with pride he fall into the same condemnation as the devil. Moreover he must have a good testimony among those who are outside, lest he fall into reproach and the snare of the devil. Likewise deacons must be reverent, not double-tongued, not given to much wine, not greedy for money, holding the mystery of the faith with a pure conscience. But let these also first be tested; then let them serve as deacons, being found blameless. [NKJV 1–10]

We have heard of the Proverbs 31 woman, which represents the ideal woman. Paul's list to Timothy shows us what the ideal man looks like. None of us may match up to this perfectly, but it should be our goal because it is what God says. **Remember, progress is more important than perfection;** so you should be progressing toward the goal no matter how long it takes to get there, or even if you never get there. Any step toward this goal is a good step and makes you better than you were before.

I, too, am on this journey: I have not achieved perfection, but it has been a great ride. There are some elements I fulfill perfectly and there are others I am working on every day. Each of us should work on ourselves so that we become more like what God wants us to be. The Bible says we should be transformed by the renewing of our minds.[17] This means we must constantly remind ourselves of what we are supposed to be like and keep moving toward that goal.

The honorable man knows how to treat women

Many men grow up today without a sense of how to treat a woman. I grew up rough and was abusive in my relationships with women, but when I discovered the Kingdom of God, I changed my behavior and attitude and began to treat women like they are supposed to be treated.

Here is how the honorable man treats women:

- The honorable man protects women from harm or danger and shields them from oppressors and oppression or harm.
- The honorable man opens doors for ladies, pulls their chairs so they can sit, holds their hands, and puts his arms around them so that they feel assured and reassured.

---

17   Romans 12:2.

- The honorable man lifts the heavy things, opens the hard-to-open bottles, takes out the garbage.

- The honorable man is protective and supportive; he keeps the women around him safe and assured.

The honorable man knows how to love a woman

The Bible instructs husbands to love their wives.[18] To love women, a real man must learn about women. Women are different from men; their needs are different. We must learn the idiosyncrasies of the woman and be prepared to put into practice the keys we learn about them.

The honorable man is a family man

If you are married or plan to get married, the Bible says you should be the husband of one wife. The honorable husband is helpful, understanding, supportive, believes, appreciates, and never disappears.

H.U.S.B.A.N.D.
Helpful. **U**nderstanding. **S**upportive.
Believes. **A**ppreciates. **N**ever. **D**isappears.

The honorable man leads

There is a difference between a man doing great things and a man being great. A man will never become great by doing great things; a man will become great by being a great person (man). God Himself said that the man is supposed to lead. It is not that the man must lead in every situation; it is that God has *positioned*—

---

18   Ephesians 5:25.

set up—*the man* to lead. Learning to lead is a part of the man's purpose. God gave a role to the man and to the woman, and to the man he said you are to lead your house. A man should seek to be a leader in the home, on the job, and in society. The man's leadership role is not a matter of man being better than woman; it is about man recognizing and taking up his God-assigned position. God shared this about Abraham to show how He works in the earth:

> *And the Lord said, "Shall I hide from Abraham what I am doing, [18] since Abraham shall surely become a great and mighty nation, and all the nations of the Earth shall be blessed in him? [19] For I have known him, in order that he may <u>command his children and his household after him, that they keep the way of the Lord</u>, to do righteousness and justice, that the Lord may bring to Abraham what He has spoken to him."*

> —Genesis 18:17–19 nkjv
> (Emphasis added by the author.)

To lead you have to be a disciple (student), one who takes notes and one who imparts. Real men are teachers. Are you a student, a researcher, and a learner? Do you take notes? To lead, you should take notes so that you can impart information to others. As a man, and especially as a father, you will have "teachable moments" to benefit yourself and your family. Therefore you must take notes. A man needs knowledge to teach, because you cannot teach what you do not know.

One of the things I did with my family as soon as my children were old enough to understand was to lead family devotions and family meetings. I taught them the Word of God because I knew what God said, and I taught them about life. They did not have to wait to get information from school or friends; I had open conversations with them and allowed them to ask questions. To lead you must have knowledge.

Here are some subjects on which men must have knowledge:

- Knowledge of Women
- Knowledge of Wife (This is different from knowing about women.)
- Knowledge of Family
- Knowledge of Business
- Knowledge of Social Issues
- Knowledge of Politics

The honorable man has influence

A real man will influence. All men will influence, but the difference is that the honorable man influences for the good. A real man will influence his environment for good when he shows up. He must show up, stand up, or shut up.

Show up - You cannot influence if you are not present. To influence you must be there in the lives of your children and your family. You cannot disappear for long periods then reappear seeking relevance. If you do not show up, your influence will not be felt. I remember a basketball player who was being interviewed sharing that he had not seen his father since he was a child, but the father showed up when he got a big contract. What a sad case. The young man stated that he was not giving his father anything because he never showed up for him.

Stand up - Once you show up, you need to stand up. You need to stand up for your family, stand up for your values. We are living in a time where the authority and autonomy of the family is being challenged. Governments and various interest groups are targeting children as if they brought them into the world and are their parents. Do not allow anyone to take advantage of your children; be there to protect them from evil. Be there to make sure no one is taking advantage of them.

Shut up - If you do not show up or stand up, then you need to shut up because whatever you say is noise at that point. So many young men have said to me, "I do not want to hear from my father because he was never there. Since he never showed up or stood up, he needs to shut up."

Never forget that you, the man, are the key. Without you your wife, family, children are all disadvantaged. The influence of men is desperately needed; in too many homes, women are the primary influence on children while the men are too often missing. The man needs to take his rightful place and influence the destiny not only of children and families but of nations. If men are on drugs, in prison, in gangs, under the haze of alcohol or drugs, and outside the church, it means a massive hole exists in society that no one else can fill.

During a conversation with a young lady who was in college, I asked how life was going and if she was in a relationship. She stated that her class consisted of thirty-two students and of the thirty-two, twenty-eight were females and one of the young men was not interested in women. Hers is a sad scenario that is played out in many areas of the world, particularly in Black communities. Women are showing up to become doctors, lawyers, engineers, social workers, business executives, while the men are on the streets and in prison in disproportionate numbers.

Years ago, men stepped up through organizations like Boys' Brigade, Boy Scouts, Boys Club, and various mentoring programs. Many of these programs are under resourced, have severely declined, or are on the verge of extinction because men are not where they should be. Today it is often the women who show up at PTA meetings, the games, the recitals, the soccer events, or church. Women are outnumbering men in both the college and professional arena, meaning, women are present at birth, during childhood, into adulthood, in the community, and even in the political arena.

Women are showing up and men are not. God never meant for women to be the primary influencers; He saw a team and He picked the husband and father to lead, yet the man has gone missing. **Let's face it, the world will not get any better until men get better.** Women are already punching well above their weight and the men are on the sidelines watching them, at times even adding to their burden by becoming dependents, just like children, or even worse, taking from women who are already the breadwinners and providers and nurturers. **A woman cannot give what is assigned to the man; the man must show up in order to influence.**

In my own life, my father was there in the early days, but as I grew he vanished from my life. His lack of influence caused me to fall under the influence of men on the streets who became my surrogate fathers and led me on a worse path than my father was on. When the day came that my life was changed, I vowed to be the influence on my children that I had lacked as a child. So I showed up from day one. When each of my children was born, I told my wife, "You went through enough to have this baby, I will wake up in the night to take care of them while you rest." I took my children to school, went to their games, played, prayed and studied with them, and guided them. My influence was heavy and resulted in them having a balanced view of life. They had a mother and a father who poured into them. They understood the importance of a father and what a father provides, and this gave them a head start which they rode to great success in life. Mister, your influence is critical. You must be there. You are the key to the future success and stability of your family, community and world.

8 | PMF—PURSUE, MAXIMIZE, FULFILL

When Jesus wanted [When the time came for Jesus] to fix the world, He strategically chose men. He gave twelve men the task of changing history and creating a new order. Those twelve dedicated men accomplished the most impossible feat. Without government support, significant financial backers, or political affiliation, they turned the world upside down. Real man, you are chosen just like The Twelve to make a difference and change the world. To do so you must do three things:

1. Pursue your purpose
2. Maximize your potential
3. Fulfill your destiny

Pursue your purpose

The Bible says that before you were born, God knew you by name; before you were conceived, he had a plan for your life. Growing up, you did not know God's plan for your life, and maybe you still do not know. That plan is the key to your life. You are here for a purpose and God has plans for you, but until you connect with Him, you will wander aimlessly from relationship to relationship, from problem to problem, from excitement to disappointment. You will never fulfill your destiny until you discover YOUR purpose.

Only God can reveal your purpose to you. Notice the words "before you were born" and "I know the plans" which God spoke to Jeremiah:

> "Before I formed you in the womb I knew you;
> <u>Before you were born</u> I sanctified you;
> I ordained you a prophet to the nations."

Then said I:

> "Ah, Lord God!
> Behold, I cannot speak, for I am a youth."

But the Lord said to me:

> "Do not say, 'I am a youth,'
> For you shall go to all to whom I send you,
> And whatever I command you, you shall speak.
> Do not be afraid of their faces,
> For I am with you to deliver you," says the Lord.

Then the Lord put forth His hand and touched my mouth, and the Lord said to me:

> "Behold, I have put My words in your mouth.
> See, I have this day set you over the nations and over the kingdoms,
> To root out and to pull down,
> To destroy and to throw down,
> To build and to plant."

> —Jeremiah 1:5–10 nkjv

"For <u>I know the plans I have for you</u>," declares the Lord, "plans to prosper you and not to harm you, plans to give you hope and a future."

—Jeremiah 29:11 niv

How do you discover your purpose? God gives us purpose indicators to point us in the direction we are to go. These purpose indicators include talents, gifts, abilities, and interests. Are there things [specific opportunities, demands, requests] that keep coming back [up] in your life? They may be purpose indicators. Why does a bird have wings? Because its purpose is to fly. Do you have the talent to run fast or to run long distances? You are supposed to use that talent as an indicator of your purpose.

Remember this: Whatever God gives you is His gift to you. What you do with it is your gift back to Him. When God has given you something and you never use it or develop it, you are insulting God. He fashioned you, gave you a purpose, made plans for you and you waste it all by doing something goofy? God will reveal your purpose through the stages and events of your life. Remember this: "When purpose is not known, abuse is inevitable."[19] You must discover your purpose, or you will live unfulfilled.

Maximize your potential

Once you have discovered your purpose, you must then maximize your potential. God places in each of us potential, or unreleased power, that has to be understood and developed so that it can be maximized for the benefit of those we were born to impact

---

19 Myles Munroe, *Understanding the Power and Purpose of Woman.* New Kensington, PA: Whitaker House, 2001.

[influence]. David had the potential to be king of Israel. He discovered his potential in the bushes before being thrust onto the big stage of life, where his potential was maximized and released to the world. Like David, I was born to be something special, but my potential was untapped and undeveloped because I did not know my purpose. When I made the connection to my Source and discovered my purpose and potential, it took me to my destiny. **Destiny is the original intent of God for your life.** Sometimes our lack of understanding of purpose causes a detour, but God can bring us back on track if we submit our lives to Him.

Fulfill your destiny

Your destiny is the end point of your journey. When you go to the airport to board a plane, you are asked what your destination is. **If you do not know your destination you will not be allowed to board.** In the same way, as a man, you need to know your destiny; and in order to fulfill your destiny, you first must discover your purpose, then maximize your potential. The destiny of great athletes is to win the medal or the championship. They may have the potential to win, but if they do not align potential with purpose and put in the work to maximize that potential, the potential will not result in a fulfilled destiny. As a man, this is your responsibility today: discover your purpose, maximize your potential, and in the end fulfill your destiny. Leave nothing on the table; go for your God-given destiny.

Rise to your highest level. Pursue your purpose, maximize your potential, and fulfill your destiny.

To make it to your destiny you must remember and avoid the things that can destroy a man. The Bible explains the three most common things that destroy a man:

1. Alcohol and substance abuse

2. Laziness and unproductivity

3. Carnality - chasing flesh

Here is a warning against these vices given by a mother to her son, the king:

> What, my son?
> And what, son of my womb?
> And what, son of my vows?
> Do not give your strength to women,
> Nor your ways to that which destroys kings.
>
> It is not for kings, O Lemuel,
> It is not for kings to drink wine,
> Nor for princes intoxicating drink;
> Lest they drink and forget the law,
> And pervert the justice of all the afflicted.
> Give strong drink to him who is perishing,
> And wine to those who are bitter of heart.
> Let him drink and forget his poverty,
> And remember his misery no more.

—Proverbs 31:1–7

Idle hands can cause one to be distracted and drawn away into fruitless pursuits. Men must remember that women are not game to be hunted and exploited. Women are not sport. Women are there to HELP you become the man were born to be.

Jesus made some very simple yet profound statements about purpose. He said a man needs to be born again to see the Kingdom: *"But seek first the kingdom of God and His righteousness, and all these things shall be added to you"* (Matthew 6:33). **The**

real man must understand these words and seek, pursue, and find the Kingdom because the Kingdom of God is where he belongs.

The Kingdom of God has a code of conduct: it is the culture of Heaven that Jesus said must come to earth. God extends the culture of Heaven to earth through the man. Therefore, this journey we are on is about revealing and reflecting the King, His Kingdom, and the Royal Family of which we all are a part. The Bible tells us we are "joint heirs with Christ,"[20] which means co-rulers. When you are born again into the Kingdom of God, you become a partner with Jesus Himself in extending the culture of Heaven to earth.

There is a tremendous reward in being a good man, a godly man, an honorable man, a real man. Decide today to discover and pursue your purpose, maximize your potential, and fulfill your destiny.

---

20   Romans 8:17.

9 | SCRIPTURES TO ENCOURAGE AND GUIDE REAL MEN

Generation of Upright Will Be Blessed

Psalm 112

Praise the Lord!

Blessed is the man who fears the Lord,
Who delights greatly in His commandments.

2 His descendants will be mighty on earth;
The generation of the upright will be blessed.
3 Wealth and riches will be in his house,
And his righteousness endures forever.
4 Unto the upright there arises light in the darkness;
He is gracious, and full of compassion, and righteous.
5 A good man deals graciously and lends;
He will guide his affairs with discretion.
6 Surely he will never be shaken;
The righteous will be in everlasting remembrance.
7 He will not be afraid of evil tidings;

His heart is steadfast, trusting in the Lord.
[8] His heart is established;
He will not be afraid,
Until he sees his desire upon his enemies.

[9] He has dispersed abroad,
He has given to the poor;
His righteousness endures forever;
His horn will be exalted with honor.
[10] The wicked will see it and be grieved;
He will gnash his teeth and melt away;
The desire of the wicked shall perish.

God, Nature and Man

Romans 1:18–25

For the wrath of God is revealed from heaven against all ungodliness and unrighteousness of men, who suppress the truth in unrighteousness, [19] because what may be known of God is manifest in them, for God has shown it to them. [20] For since the creation of the world His invisible attributes are clearly seen, being understood by the things that are made, *even* His eternal power and Godhead, so that they are without excuse. (nkjv emphasis added by the author)

[21] For although they knew God, they neither glorified him as God nor gave thanks to him, but their thinking became futile and their foolish hearts were darkened. [22] Although they claimed to be wise, they became fools [23] and exchanged the glory of the immortal God for images made to look like a mortal human being and birds and animals and reptiles.

²⁴ Therefore God gave them over in the sinful desires of their hearts to sexual impurity for the degrading of their bodies with one another. ²⁵ They exchanged the truth about God for a lie, and worshiped and served created things rather than the Creator—who is forever praised. Amen. (niv, emphasis added by the author)

Wisdom for Real Men

Proverbs 1:1–7

The proverbs of Solomon son of David, king of Israel:

² for gaining wisdom and instruction;
  for understanding words of insight;
³ for receiving instruction in prudent behavior,
  doing what is right and just and fair;
⁴ for giving prudence to those who are simple,
  knowledge and discretion to the young—
⁵ let the wise listen and add to their learning,
  and let the discerning get guidance—
⁶ for understanding proverbs and parables,
  the sayings and riddles of the wise.

⁷ The fear of the Lord is the beginning of knowledge,
  but fools despise wisdom and instruction. niv

Proverbs 1:5

A wise man will hear and increase in learning,
And a man of understanding will acquire wise counsel.

1 Timothy 4:12

Let no one look down on your youthfulness, but rather in speech, conduct, love, faith and purity, show yourself an example of those who believe.

The Strength of Men
1 John 2:14–17

I write to you, dear children,
   because you know the Father.
I write to you, fathers,
   because you know him who is from the beginning.
I write to you, young men,
   because you are strong,
   and the word of God lives in you,
   and you have overcome the evil one.

[15] Do not love the world or anything in the world. If anyone loves the world, love for the Father is not in them. [16] For everything in the world—the lust of the flesh, the lust of the eyes, and the pride of life—comes not from the Father but from the world. [17] The world and its desires pass away, but whoever does the will of God lives forever. niv

Benefits of Living Godly
Genesis 2:18

Then the Lord God said, "It is not good for the man to be alone; I will make him a helper suitable for him." niv

Genesis 2:21–25

So the Lord God caused a deep sleep to fall upon the man, and he slept; then He took one of his ribs and closed up the flesh at that place. [22] And the Lord God fashioned into a woman the rib which He had taken from the man, and brought her to the man. [23] Then the man said,

> "At last this is bone of my bones,
> And flesh of my flesh;
>
> She shall be called 'woman,'
> Because she was taken out of man."

[24] For this reason a man shall leave his father and his mother, and be joined to his wife; and they shall become one flesh. [25] And the man and his wife were both naked, but they were not ashamed. nasb

Genesis 5:2

He created them male and female, and He blessed them and named them "mankind" on the day when they were created. nasb

Proverbs 1:7

> The fear of the Lord is the beginning of knowledge,
>   but fools[21] despise wisdom and instruction.
>
> [8] Listen, my son, to your father's instruction
>   and do not forsake your mother's teaching.
> [9] They are a garland to grace your head
>   and a chain to adorn your neck.

---

21   The Hebrew words rendered fool in Proverbs denotes one who is morally deficient.

¹⁰ My son, if sinful men entice you,
    do not give in to them.
¹¹ If they say, "Come along with us;
    let's lie in wait for innocent blood,
    let's ambush some harmless soul;
¹² let's swallow them alive, like the grave,
    and whole, like those who go down to the pit;
¹³ we will get all sorts of valuable things
    and fill our houses with plunder;
¹⁴ cast lots with us;
    we will all share the loot"—
¹⁵ my son, do not go along with them,
    do not set foot on their paths;
¹⁶ for their feet rush into evil,
    they are swift to shed blood.
¹⁷ How useless to spread a net
    where every bird can see it!
¹⁸ These men lie in wait for their own blood;
    they ambush only themselves!
¹⁹ Such are the paths of all who go after ill-gotten gain;
    it takes away the life of those who get it. NIV

Lamentations 5:14

Elders are absent from the gate,
Young men from their music. NASB

1 Corinthians 11:11–12

However, in the Lord, neither is woman independent of man, nor is man independent of woman. ¹² For as the woman originated from the man, so also the man has his birth through the woman; and all things originate from God.

Man and God's Spirit

Joel 2:28-29

"It will come about after this
That I will pour out My Spirit on all mankind;
And your sons and your daughters will prophesy,
Your old men will have dreams,
Your young men will see visions.
[29] And even on the male and female servants
I will pour out My Spirit in those days."

—NASB

Men, Women and Order

Genesis 3:16

To the woman He said,
"I will greatly multiply
Your pain in childbirth,
In pain you will bring forth children;
Yet your desire will be for your husband,
And he will rule over you."

Deuteronomy 22:5

"A woman shall not wear a man's clothing, nor shall a man put on a woman's clothing; for whoever does these things is an abomination to the LORD your God. NASB

Proverbs 15:18

A hot-tempered man stirs up strife,
But the slow to anger calms a dispute.

Proverbs 18:16

A man's gift makes room for him,
And brings him before great men. NKJV

Proverbs 29:22

An angry man stirs up strife,
And a hot-tempered man abounds in transgression. NASB 1995

Luke 2:25

And there was a man in Jerusalem whose name was Simeon; and this man was righteous and devout, looking for the consolation of Israel; and the Holy Spirit was upon him. NASB 1995

1 Corinthians 11:3

But I want you to understand that Christ is the head of every man, and the man is the head of a woman, and God is the head of Christ. NASB 1995

1 Corinthians 11:2-16

Now I praise you because you remember me in everything and hold firmly to the traditions, just as I delivered them to you. But I want you to understand that Christ is the head of every man, and the man is the head of a woman, and God is the head of Christ.

1 Corinthians 11:11-12

However, in the Lord, neither is woman independent of man, nor is man independent of woman. For as the woman originates from the man, so also the man has his birth through the woman; and all things originate from God.

Colossians 3:18-21

Wives, be subject to your husbands, as is fitting in the Lord. Husbands, love your wives and do not be embittered against them. Children, be obedient to your parents in all things, for this is well-pleasing to the Lord.

Ephesians 5:22-24

Wives, be subject to your own husbands, as to the Lord. For the husband is the head of the wife, as Christ also is the head of the church, He Himself being the Savior of the body. But as the church is subject to Christ, so also the wives ought to be to their husbands in everything.

Men and Work

2 Thessalonians 3:10

For even when we were with you, we used to give you this order: if anyone is not willing to work, then he is not to eat, either.

Men and Worship

Exodus 10:11

Not so! Go now, the men among you, and serve the LORD, for that is what you desire." So they were driven out from Pharaoh's presence.

Genesis 1:27

God created man in His own image, in the image of God He created him; male and female He created them.

About The Author

His Excellency Dr. David M Burrows JP CM Global Peace Ambassador.

Pastor Dave Burrows currently serves as Senior Pastor of Bahamas Faith Ministries Church and as President of Bahamas Faith Ministries International nonprofit corporation both of which he co founded with the late world renowned visionary and leader Dr. Myles Munroe whom he succeeded. Pastor Burrows is a multifaceted author, motivator, inspirator, businessman, consultant and mentor. Burrows was a longtime close associate of Dr. Munroe for over 30 years having traveled and partnered with Dr. Munroe in many projects, events and venues while serving as Vice President of the global entity Myles Munroe International.

Dr. Burrows has a long history as a Global Youth and Family specialist, mentor, life coach and inspirational and motivational speaker consulting for Churches, Pastors, Cities, countries and numerous organizations and denominations. He has served as advisor to the Bahamas Government on Youth matters as Chairman of the National Youth Advisory Council on three occasions. He has also served as Parliamentary Chaplain to the Bahamas Government and House of Assembly. In addition to serving in his current capacity, Pastor Burrows also serves as a board member of the Empowered 21 Global Council and as Co-Chair of the Caribbean region. In 2022 he was bestowed the prestigious Companion Order of Merit as a National Hero of the Bahamas and appointed as a UN sanctioned Global Peace Ambassador by WOLMI.

Dr. Burrows grew up in Nassau Bahamas and spent his teenage years on the streets involved in the street world of violence, substance abuse and activities that caused him to be expelled from school for assaulting a teacher, put out of his home for assaulting his father and subject to many of the perils of street life. He experienced a dramatic turnaround while in his second year of College which propelled him into ministry to troubled youth and gang members.

An accomplished author Pastor Burrows has published nineteen books and served as executive producer of five movies and three music soundtracks. His works include The Laws of Good Success, Making the Most of Your Teenage Years, the Power of Positive Choices, Sex and Dating and Kingdom Parenting which he co-authored with Dr. Munroe.

He has appeared on many local and international television programs and events hosted by TBN, TD Jakes Potters Touch, Oral Roberts University, Messiah College, Prairie View A&M University, Washington College, Armstrong Williams Show, The Potter's House Denver, Crenshaw Christian Center (Dr. Fred Price) West Angeles Church of God in Christ and many others. He has spoken, consulted and conducted seminars extensively in the United States, Caribbean, Canada, The United Kingdom, Europe, Australia, New Zealand and Africa. Pastor Burrows and

Bahamas Faith Ministries have partnered over the years in staging a variety of outreaches in the Caribbean, USA, UK, Africa, Haiti, Australia, New Zealand and other countries.

In addition to Youth and Family ministry Pastor Burrows has served as a leadership, business and technology consultant for many organizations. His clients have included major local and international corporations, civic and social organizations and churches. He founded and continues to serve as president and CEO of Megabyte Computers and One Rib Publications.

Dave Burrows has mentored and coached many individuals to personal, spiritual, vocational and business success and continues to serve as Pastor, consultant, inspirational and motivational speaker and life coach.

Contact Information:

www.davidburrowsinternational.com

pastordaveburrows@hotmail.com

242-461-6475, 954-815-1538, 242-357-4492

Social media contacts:

Youtube channel Dave Burrows,
Facebook, Twitter, Instagram

Highschool Basketball Team

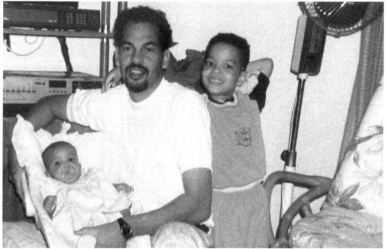

Milton Keynes UK
Ingram Content Group UK Ltd.
UKHW020745080124
435661UK00017B/958

9 781959 806110